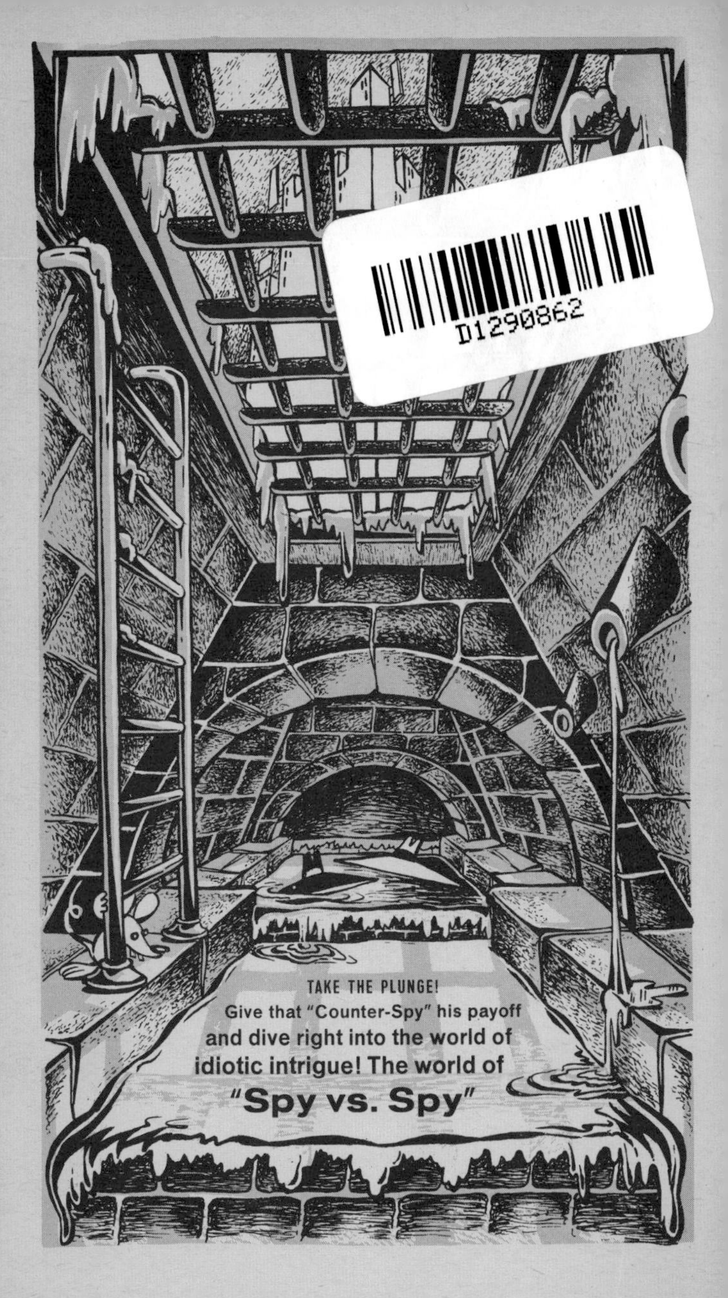
D1290862
TAKE THE PLUNGE!
Give that "Counter-Spy" his payoff
and dive right into the world of
idiotic intrigue! The world of
"Spy vs. Spy"

MAD'S
SPY
VS
SPY
SIGNET
BOOKS
A SIGNET BOOK
Published by THE NEW AMERICAN LIBRARY,
New York and Toronto
THE NEW ENGLISH LIBRARY Limited,
London

FOLLOW-UP FILE
by
ANTONIO PROHIAS
Edited by
ALBERT B. FELDSTEIN
With a Foreword By
Jerry De Fuccio

SIGNET TRADEMARK REG. U.S. PAT. OFF. AND FOREIGN COUNTRIES
REGISTERED TRADEMARK—MARCA REGISTRADA
HECHO EN CHICAGO, U.S.A.

SIGNET BOOKS are published *in the United States* by
The New American Library, Inc.,
1301 Avenue of the Americas, New York, New York 10019,
in Canada by The New American Library of Canada Limited,
295 King Street East, Toronto 2, Ontario,
in the United Kingdom by The New English Library Limited,
Barnard's Inn, Holborn, London, E.C. 1, England

FIRST PRINTING, APRIL, 1968

PRINTED IN THE UNITED STATES OF AMERICA

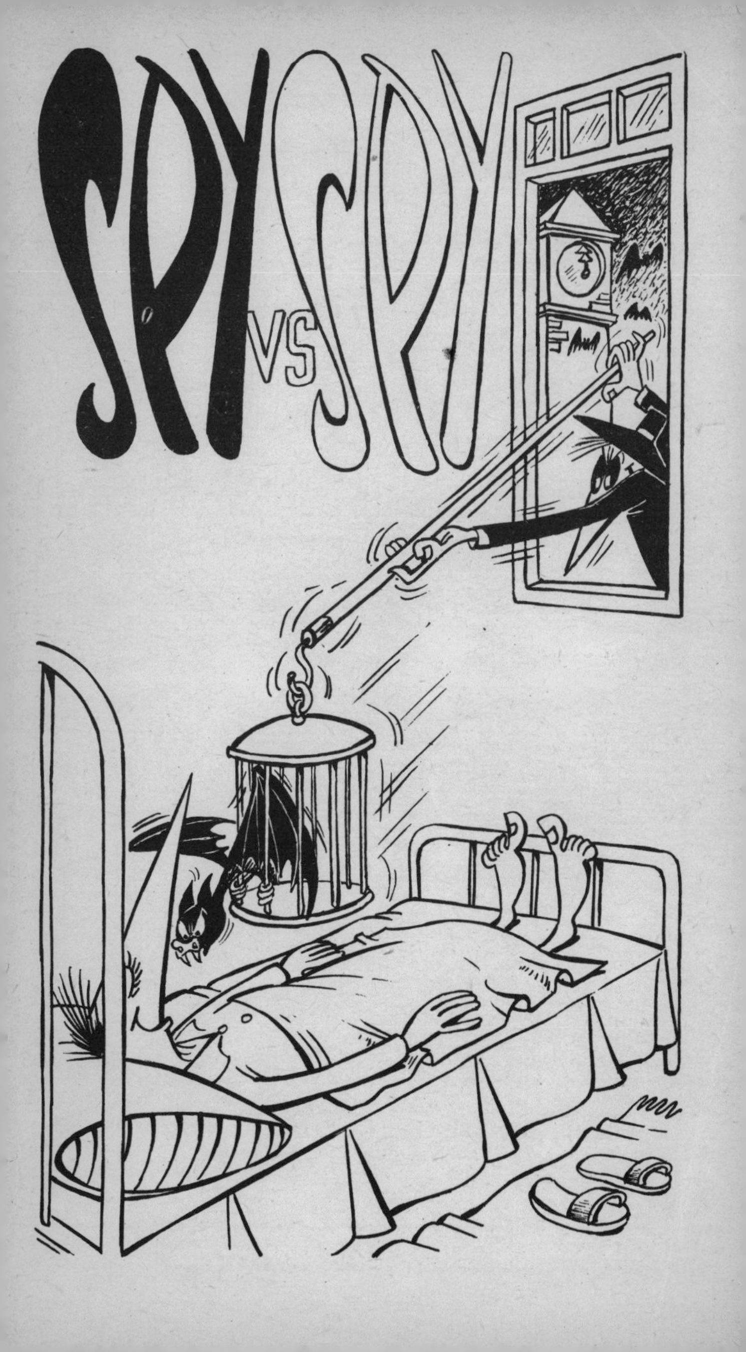
SPY VS SPY

CODE

CODE

BOOM!

SPY
VS
SPY

SPY
SPY

SPY VS SPY
PREMIERE

SPY VS SPY
PREMIERE

PREMIERE
RADAR

SPY
VS
SPY

EMBASSY

EMBASSY

EMBASSY

RING
EMBASSY

EMBAS

EMBASS

EMBASSY

EMBASSY

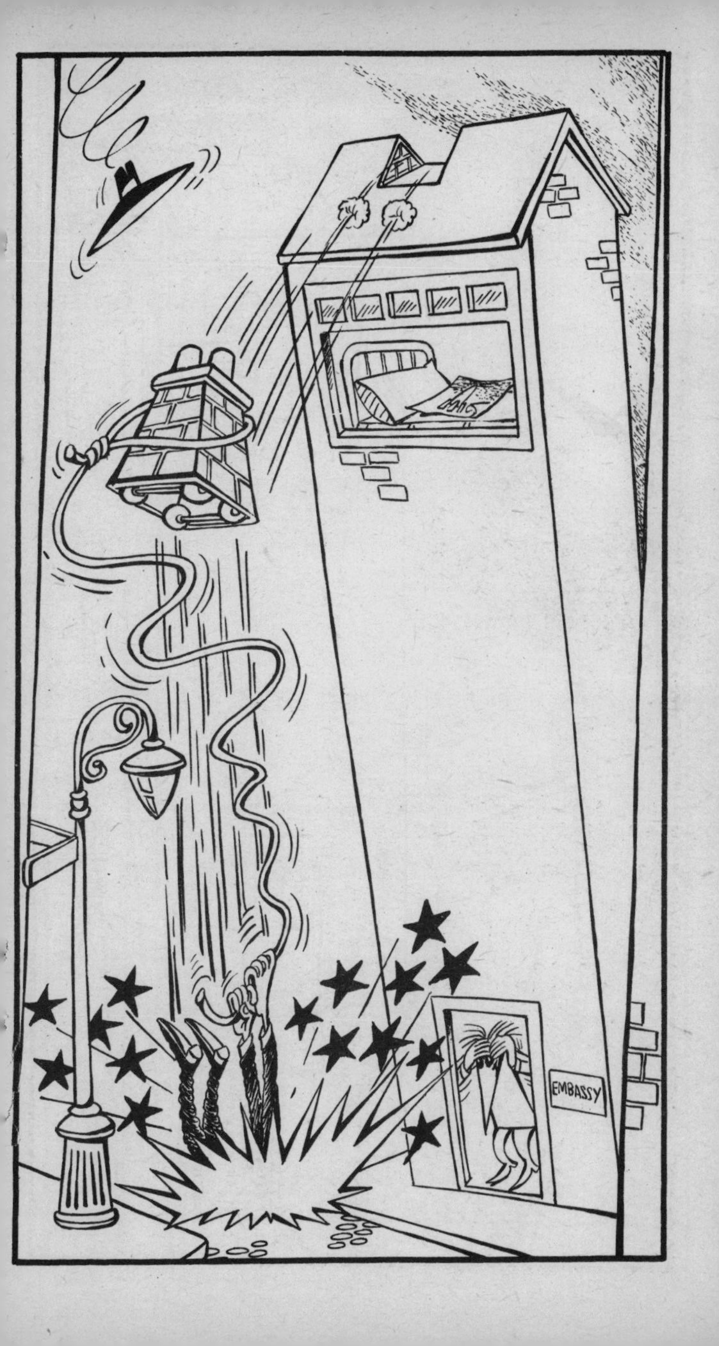
EMBASSY

EMBASSY

EMBASSY

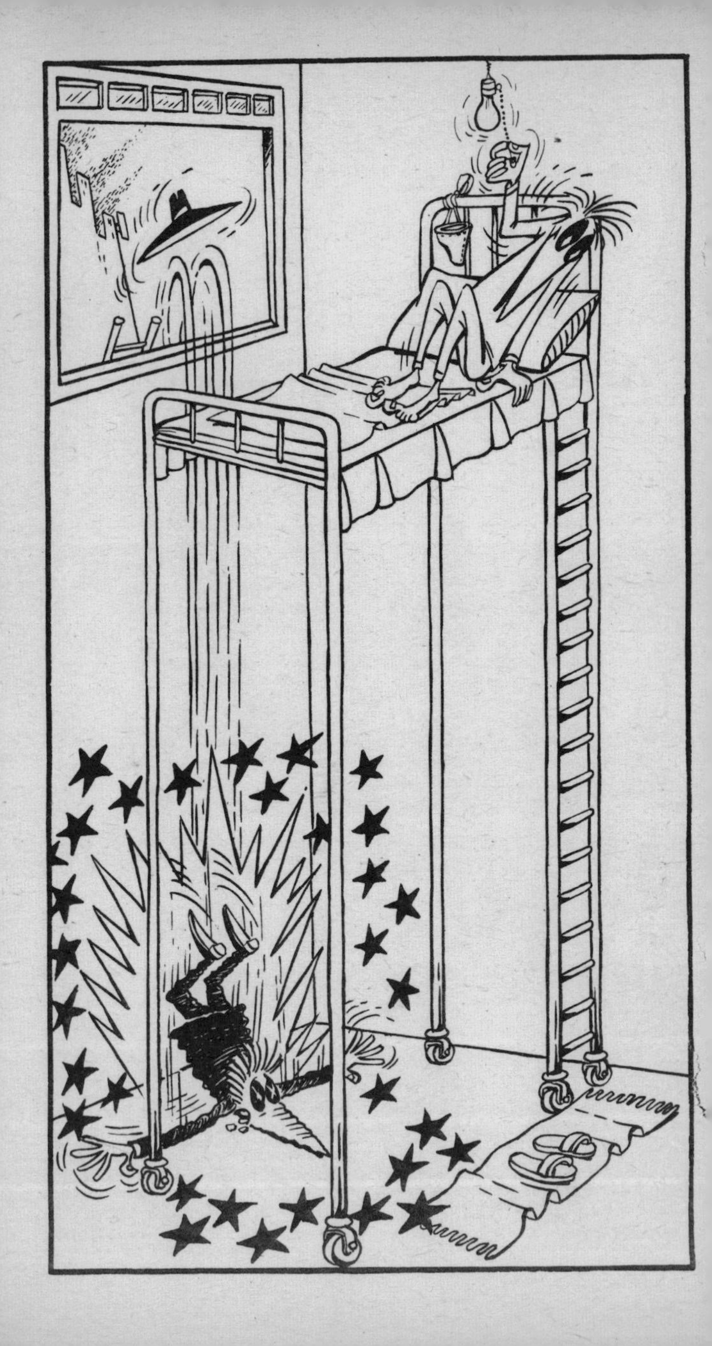

SPY
VS
SPY

VOODOO

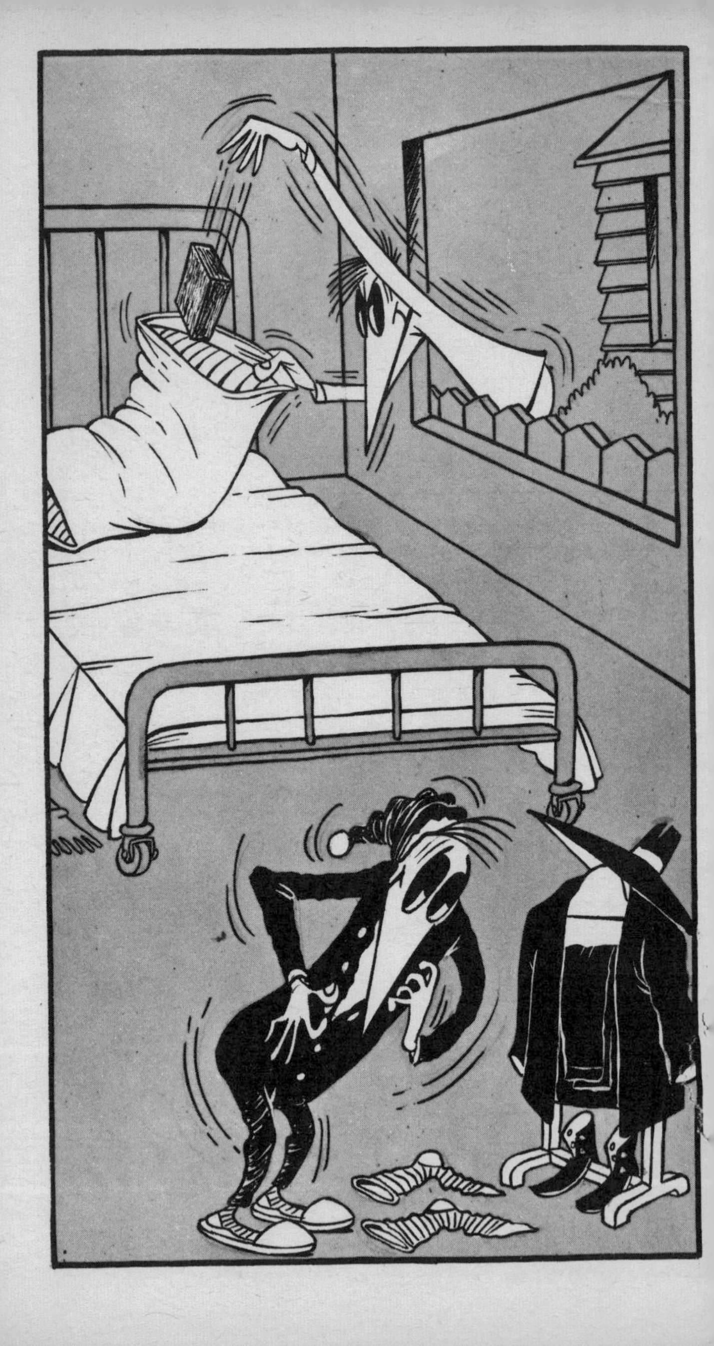

BOOM

SPY VS SPY

EXTRA
NEW WHITE SUB
RULES THE SEAS

20-8-5
20-9
?

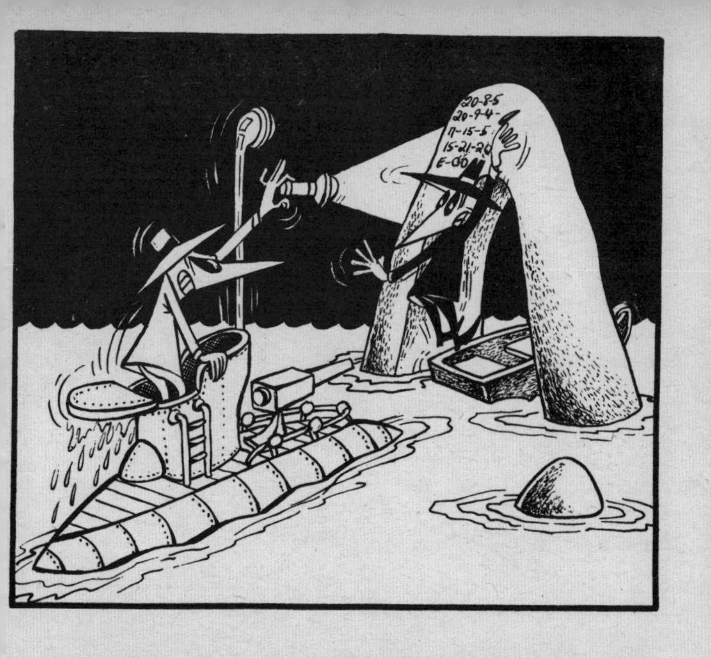
20-8-5
20-9-4-
7-15-5
15-21-20

20-8-5
20-9-4-5
7-15-5-19
15-21-20
E-AA-1-13
19-15-18-16-15-9-19-5

20-8-5
20-9-4-5
7-15-5-19
15-21-20
E-AA-1-13
19-15-18-16-15-9-19-5

20-8-5
20-9-4-5
7-15-5-19
15-21-20
E-AA-1-13
19-15-18-16-15-9-19-5
CODE

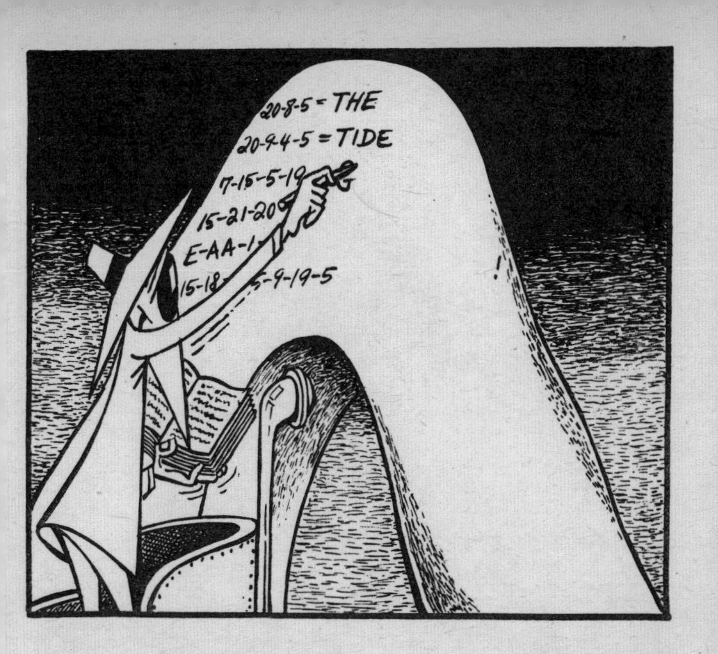
20-8-5 = THE
20-9-4-5 = TIDE
7-15-5-19
15-21-20
E-AA-1-
15-18
5-9-19-5
!

20-8-5 = THE
20-9-4-5 = TIDE
7-15-5-19 = GOES
15-21-20 = OUT
E-AA-1-13 = 6:00 AM
19-15-18-16-15-9-19-5 = SURPRISE !
?

THE
20-9-4-5= TIDE
GOES
OUT
6:50 AM
SURPRISE!
CODE

SPY vs SPY

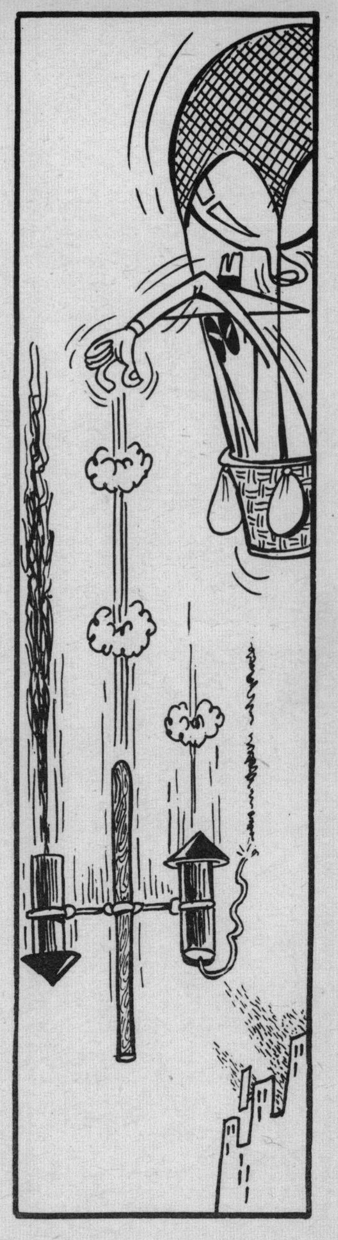

PLAF

SPY VS SPY
TOP SECRET

BANK
$

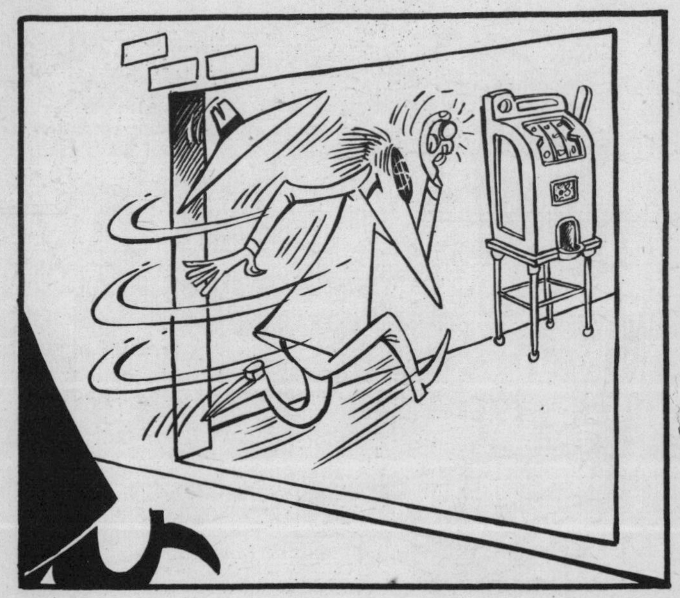

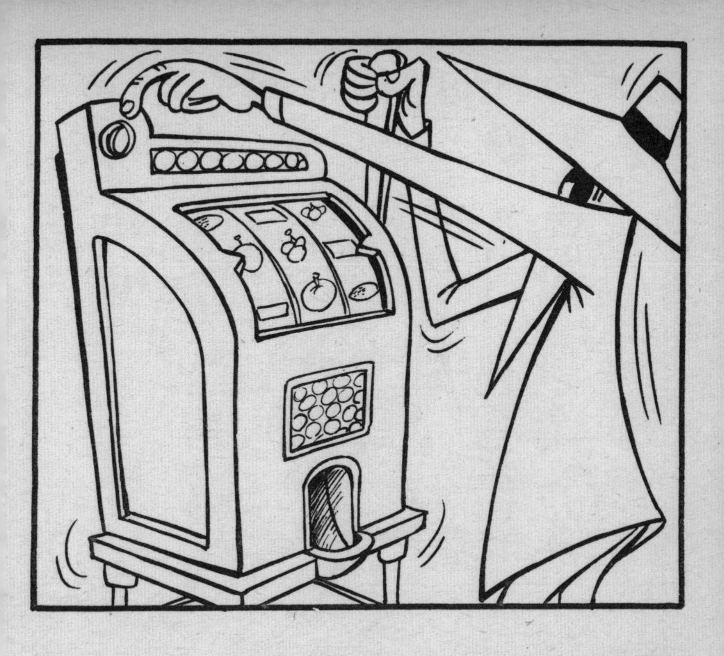

CLINK
CLINK
CLINK

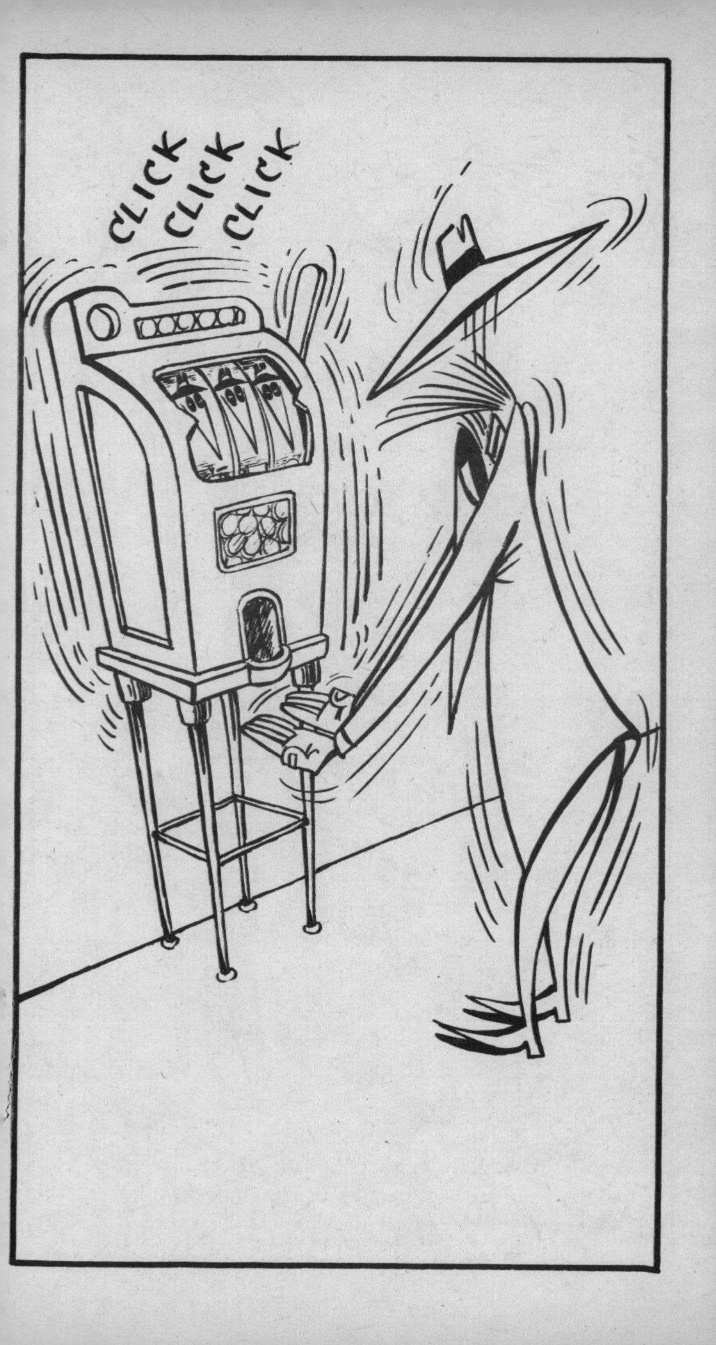
CLICK
CLICK
CLICK

BOOM!
BOOM!
BOOM!
BOOM!
BOOM!

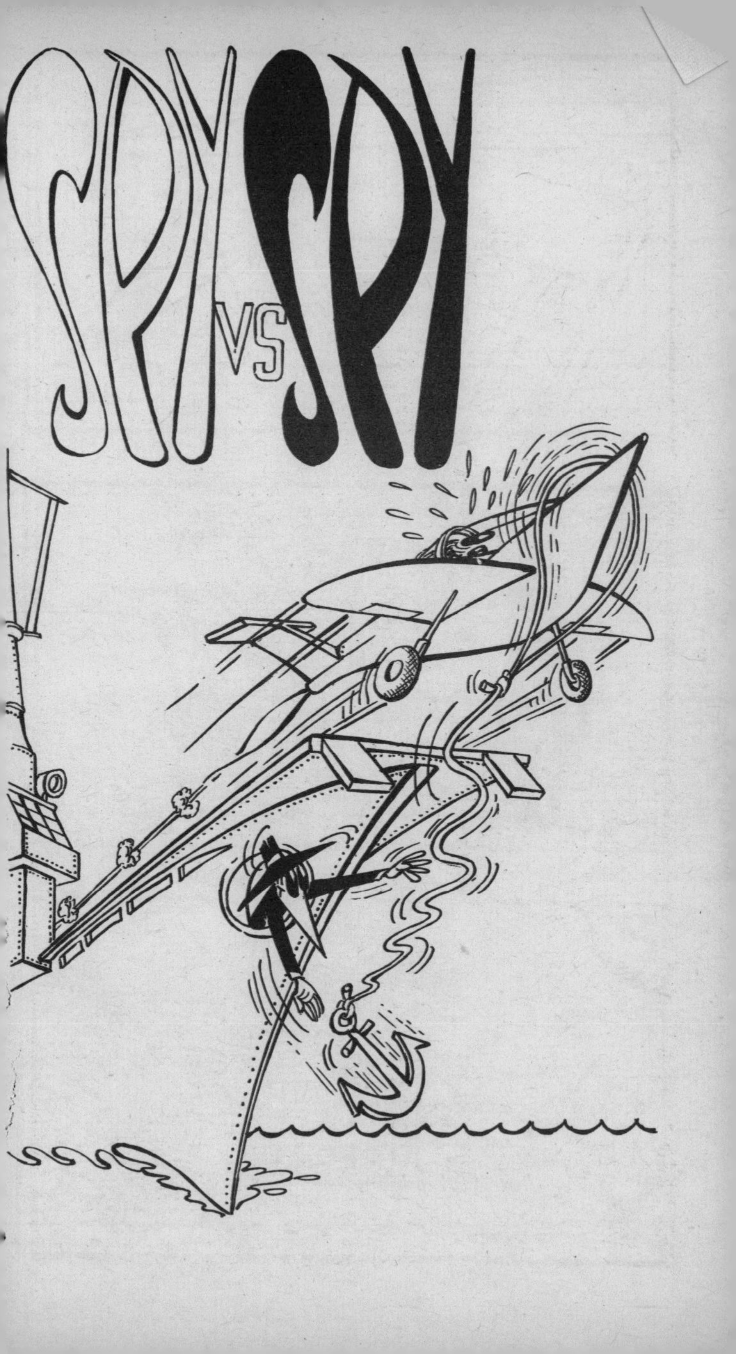
SPY vs SPY

VIA AIR MAIL

VIA AIR MAIL

?
VIA AIR MAIL
AIRPORT

AIR MAIL
?

AIR MAIL

CLICK

VIA AIR MAIL

VIA AIR MAIL

SPY
VS
SPY

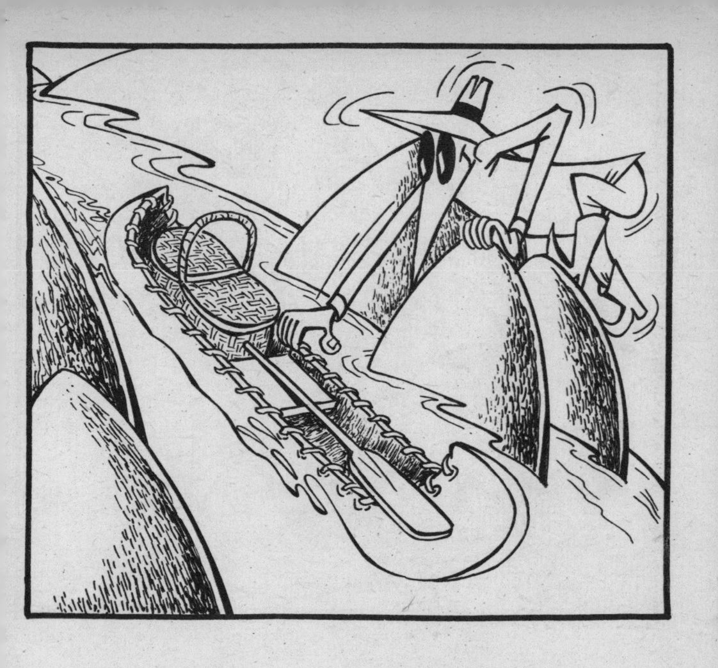

STICK 'EM UP!

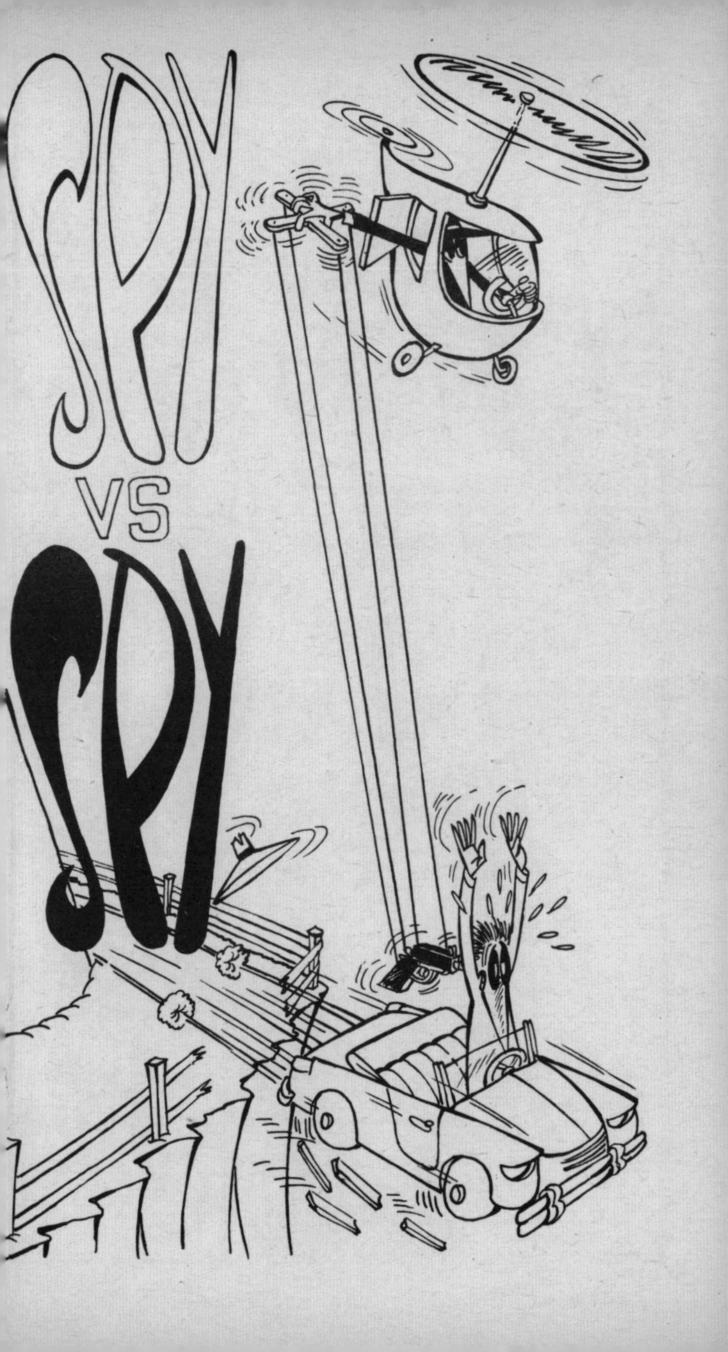
SPY
VS
SPY

SPY VS SPY

WANTED
DEAD OR ALIVE

PLASTIC SURGERY

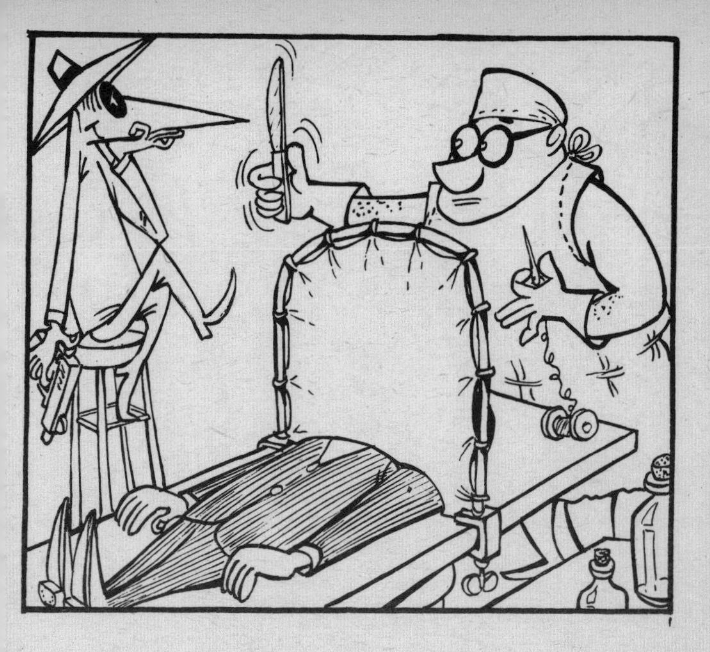

SPY

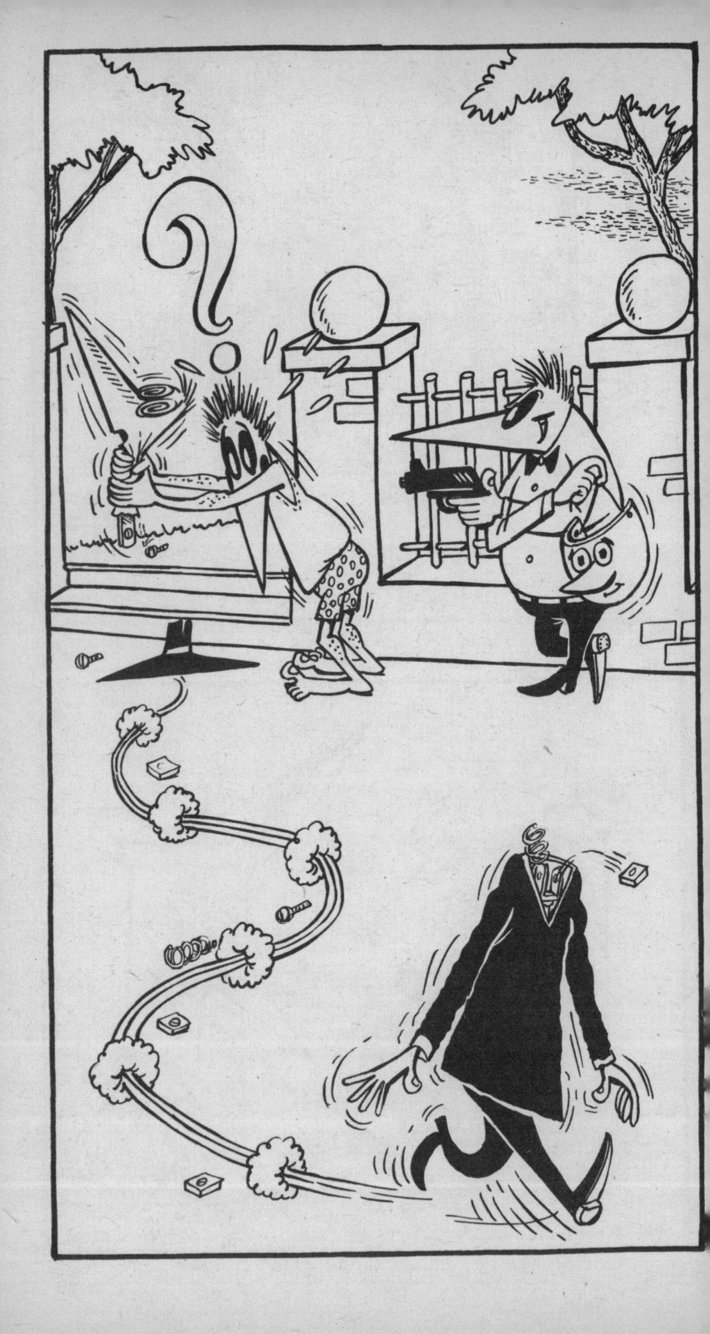

SPY
VS
SPY

TESTING
GROUNDS

TOY & NOVELTY
MFR & IMPORTER with broad exp, has high five figure tax loss, seeks connection in allied field. 28331 Times
IF YOU HAVE A GOOD PRODUCT
"LET THE PROFESSIONALS DO
FRANCHISING TAKES KNOW
COSTUME Jewelry

MERGER WANTED
A Hot Line

ARTIST
$50 TO $150
WE ACT AS YOUR N. Y. OF
$5.00 PER MONT
CONTINENTAL PHONE MA
MAIL ORDER PRO creates successful
BANDMAN ADV.
$75 Product Publicit
BUSINESS.

WORK WANTED
FOR SALE-
AMPINGS
TOOLING
ON MOLDING
PRESS HARRIS 20" CU
DOWN PAYMENT, NO IN
EASY PAYMENT
ATF 17 ½x22½ DE REBUIL
ATF 23x33 OFFSET PRESS
KLUGE 12x18 w/roll leaf attchmnt.
HEIDELBERG 10x15 late style.
CLYDESDALE process camera 17x17.
HARRIS 17x22½ LTV streamfed
ILLNESS.
WESTCHESTER-
DRUG STORES
TECHNICA

BLOW MOLD'G W
ECONOMIZE on precision parts to your
Reishauer Gear Grinding Avail
AUTOMATION
DIE CUTTING for the trade.
Cutting on Plastics, Paper
PAPER CUTT
SELL US — 14 PT
MUST SELL camera, platemaking
BEST OFFER
LAUNDROMAT
& Lines

(small busn)
WIG Beauty Shop
Top NY location
$10,000 cash down
turnover & night storage
BUSY candy store
QUEENS new
FRANKS-Drinks
rmet Gift Delicacy

PUM!

SPY
VS
SPY

SPY VS SPY

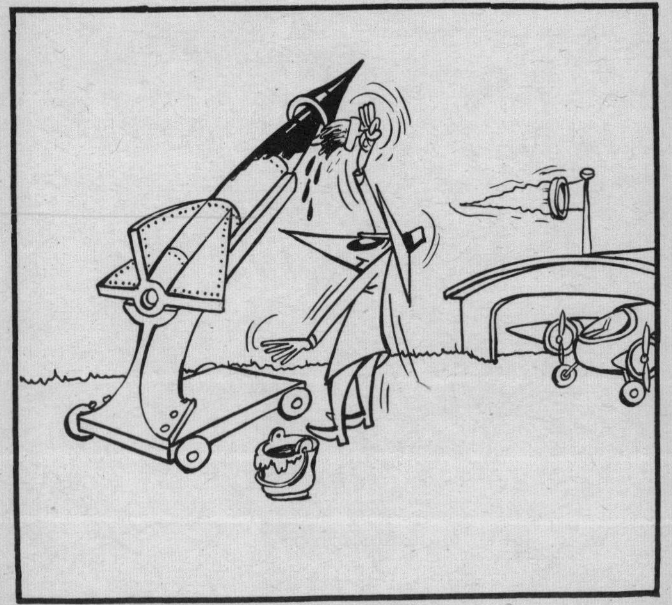

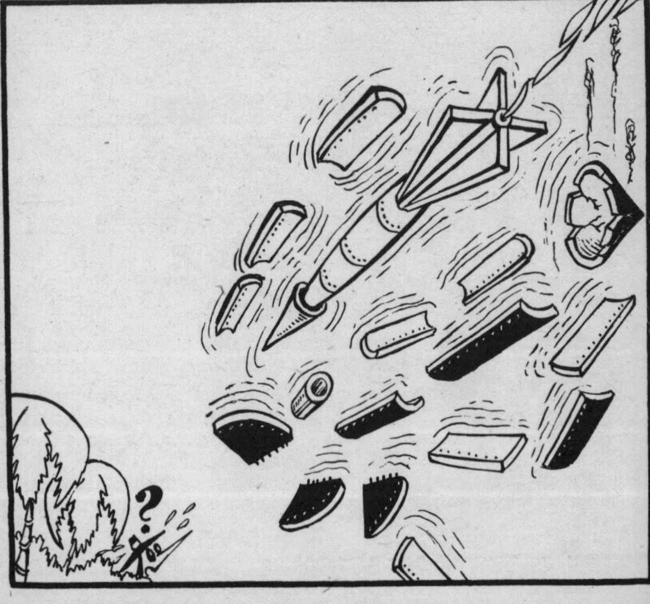

BOOM

SPY VS SPY

BUS

BUS

BU

BUS

BUS

BUS

BUS

SPY VS SPY
FREE!

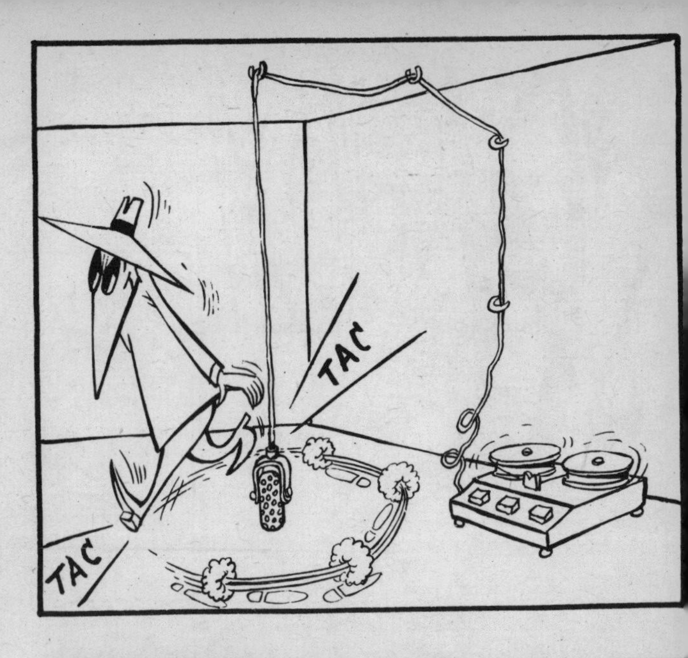
TAC
TAC

TAC
TAC

TAC

TAC

TAC

TAC
TAC

TAC
TAC

SPY vs SPY

CLICK

CLICK

SPY VS SPY

MAIL COLLECTION
11.00P.M.
TICK
TICK

MAIL

MAIL
MAIL

MAIL
EMBASSY

EMBASSY
EMBASSY MAIL

EMBASSY MAIL

TICK
TICK

TICK
TICK
TICK
EMBASS

TICK
TICK
TICK
TICK
TICK

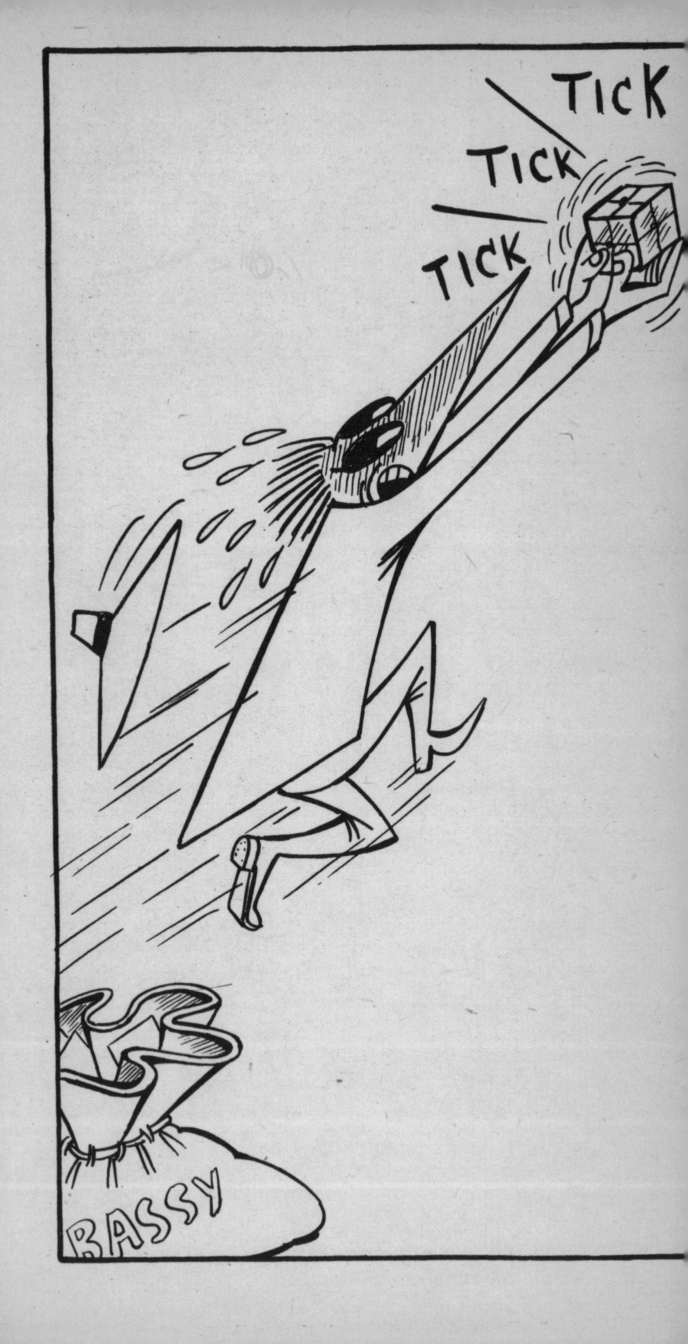
TICK
TICK
TICK
BASSY

SPY vs SPY
THE END